Multiplication
Facts in Seven Days

by Dr. Carl H. Seltzer

x	0	1	2	3	4	5	6	7	8	9
0	0	0	0	0	0	0	0	0	0	0
1	0	1	2	3	4	5	6	7	8	9
2	0	2	4	6	8	10	12	14	16	18
3	0	3	6	9	12	15	18	21	24	27
4	0	4	8	12	16	20	24	28	32	36
5	0	5	10	15	20	25	30	35	40	45
6	0	6	12	18	24	30	36	42	48	54
7	0	7	14	21	28	35	42	49	56	63
8	0	8	16	24	32	40	48	56	64	72
9	0	9	18	27	36	45	54	63	72	81

Day 5, Learn the Fours

$4 \times 5 = 20$

$4 \times 6 = 24$

$4 \times 7 = 28$

$4 \times 8 = 32$

$4 \times 9 = 36$

Do **Lesson 5** and send home **Letter E**. Review squares, twos, fives and threes.

2. $3 \times 3 =$

3. $4 \times 4 =$

4. $5 \times 5 =$

5. $6 \times 6 =$

6. $7 \times 7 =$

7. $8 \times 8 =$

8. $9 \times 9 =$

9. $8 \times 8 =$

10. $7 \times 7 =$

11. $6 \times 6 =$

12. $5 \times 5 =$

13. $4 \times 4 =$

14. $3 \times 3 =$

Didax Educational Resources
www.didax.com

Printed in the United States of America.

This book is printed on recycled paper.

Order Number 2-5293
ISBN 978-1-58324-275-9

K L M N O 17 16 15 14 13

395 Main Street
Rowley, MA 01969
www.didax.com

Multiplication Facts in Seven Days

Foreword

Students need certain facts at their disposal when doing mathematics, such as the addition facts to 20 and multiplication facts. Research shows that children's instant recall of these basic number facts will only progress from short-term memory (easily forgotten) to the long-term memory through constant practice and reinforcement.

Multiplication Facts in Seven Days offers an easy-to-follow systematic program to promote the learning of these essential number facts. Easily incorporated into any weekly program, teachers introduce the facts, which are then reinforced at home. Letters to parents are included in the book, which clearly state the facts to be practiced that day.

Strategies are included to help reduce the number of facts to be learned. Students will be happy to know that only thirty-six times tables need to be memorized to master all of the multiplication tables!

Multiplication Facts in Seven Days is an ideal mathematics support program, which allows students to achieve instant recall and understanding of number facts. Students will enjoy challenging both themselves and each other, as they work towards learning the set of number facts for each day.

Contents

Multiplication Facts in Seven Days

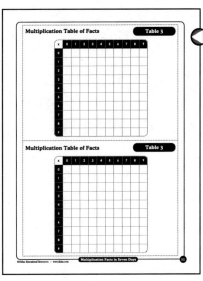

Students are introduced to the facts by completing a blank multiplication table. Patterns and rules are discussed.

Teacher notes clearly state the facts to be introduced and learned each day.

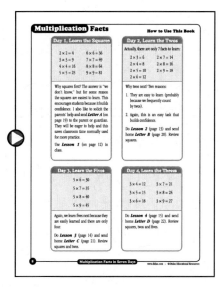

Students complete an activity page that includes the new facts and reviews previously introduced facts.

Strategies are taught to help reduce the number of facts to be learned— students need only learn four new facts to master the four times table.

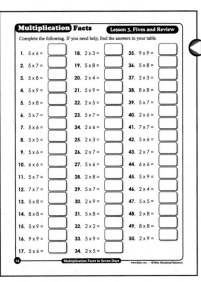

A corresponding letter is sent home with the students. Parents are involved in the practice and reinforcement stage of the program.

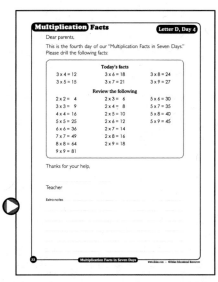

Assessment

Students complete final assessment tasks to monitor the facts learned and to discover which facts require further practice. Tests can be given periodically to keep the facts fresh in the students' minds.

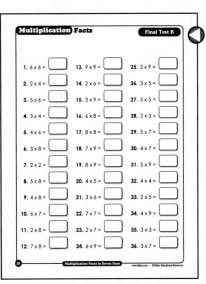

Once a student has mastered the facts, use a timer to record speed and accuracy. Challenge students to improve on their results each time a test is taken.

Choose from the three multiplication tests included.

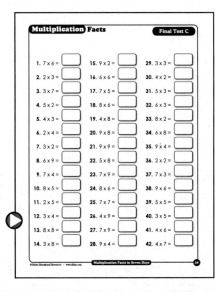

One of the most important skills students need is a mastery of the basic computational skills.

All people require the ability to mentally compute basic addition and multiplication facts quickly and accurately. It is also very important for students to understand all they can about addition and multiplication and how they relate. Students should use manipulatives to help them reinforce their understanding of the concepts.

This book does not purposely mean to address the use of manipulatives, but students need to experience the concepts involved prior to memorizing facts.

Firstly, I would like to distinguish between a fact and an algorithm.

*A **fact** is a piece of information that is accepted as true. In mathematics there are many facts that students are required to learn. Hopefully they will already have some understanding of the facts and what they mean. In mathematics, facts are usually memorized. Some examples of math facts are addition facts, multiplication facts and definitions.*

*An **algorithm** is a systematic method to solve a problem … a rule. While algorithms use facts, there is a difference between the two.*

$9 \times 12 = 108$ is an algorithm involving the facts 9×2 and 9×1 (the 1 being in 10s place), yielding $18 + 90 = 108$.

Therefore, it is never necessary to memorize 12×13, etc., because this product is produced by an algorithm.

It is helpful for students to complete a blank addition or multiplication table themselves, providing them with a better understanding of how to read these tables (See Table 3, page 11).

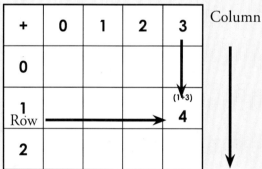

Students can use any method they wish to complete the table, but you may need to point out that where a column and a row intersect is where the sum or product is placed.

Younger students may use manipulatives such as Unifix® cubes, or counting on their fingers to find the sums or products. Older students may also use manipulatives or arrays to find sums or products. For example, an array of dots that is 3×5 would contain 15 dots.

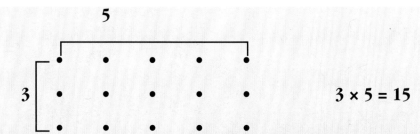

$3 \times 5 = 15$

There are many facts and skills a student needs to have at their disposal when doing mathematics, but none are more important than the multiplication facts.

One needs to know addition facts too, but can use counting-on techniques and other strategies to add 9 and 6. But, multiplying 9×6 requires not only an understanding what that means, but in my opinion, an immediate response. Of course, one could add nine sixes or six nines, but that isn't easy for many students. The solution is to memorize the multiplication facts early and quickly.

As a math educator, I have tried various approaches and have had teachers propose many different ways to help students memorize the multiplication facts, but none as effective as my "**Seven Day**" method.

I am also aware that memorizing anything in mathematics without understanding is not appropriate.

Therefore, prior to applying my **Seven Day** system, I strongly suggest that teachers are certain that their students have been given the appropriate background so they understand what multiplication is.

Also, before beginning my **Seven Day** program, there are three math principles which students need to be aware of:

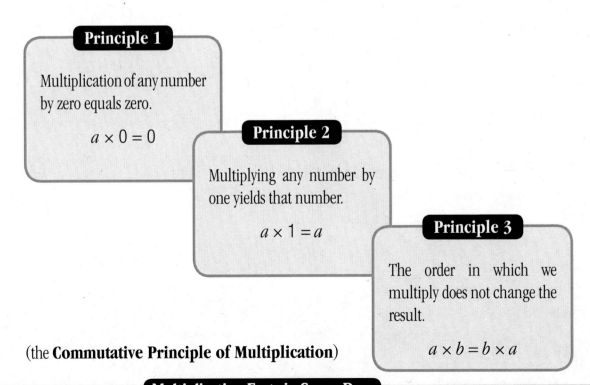

Principle 1

Multiplication of any number by zero equals zero.

$$a \times 0 = 0$$

Principle 2

Multiplying any number by one yields that number.

$$a \times 1 = a$$

Principle 3

The order in which we multiply does not change the result.

$$a \times b = b \times a$$

(the **Commutative Principle of Multiplication**)

To begin, I recommend that students be given a blank multiplication table (see **Table 3** on page 11) without the products and have them complete the table.

To complete the table they may use any prior knowledge, manipulatives, or strategy they choose. Completing the table will help them learn how to "read the table," and will allow them to discover some of the patterns in the table.

Next, give each student **Table 1** (on page 10) and discuss how the three principles allow us to black out certain facts. (See **Table 2** on page 10.) The next step is to look at **Table 2** and observe any patterns. Students may suggest a number of patterns, but there are three that need to be found:

- *First*, notice that the product of any number and zero equals zero ($a \times 0 = 0$). So we need not memorize any facts involving **zero** as a factor. (see **Table 2**)

- *Secondly*, it should be observed that one times any number, a, has a product of a ($1 \times a = a$). Therefore, we do not need to memorize any products involving one, since $1 \times a = a$: for example, $1 \times 3 = 3$, $1 \times 7 = 7$, etc. Mark out these products, as shown in **Table 2**.

- *Thirdly*, it should be observed that the products of numbers where the order is reversed is the same. For example, notice $3 \times 4 = 4 \times 3$, $6 \times 5 = 5 \times 6$ etc. Therefore, since $a \times b = b \times a$, only half of the table needs to be memorized. When you know 6×9 you know 9×6, etc.

Mark out all products that "commute," as they are the reverses of a set of products (see **Table 2**).

At this point, you will have only 36 products that have not been marked out. These are the **facts** we need to memorize.

- Note that we have eliminated $0 \times a$, because the answer is always zero. Nothing to memorize.

- Note that we have also eliminated $1 \times a$, because multiplication by one does not change anything, e.g. $1 \times a = a$.

- Note that since $a \times b = b \times a$ (order doesn't matter), only part of the facts need to be memorized. When you know $5 \times 6 = 30$, you know $6 \times 5 = 30$.

Special note: Each day, send the **Parent Letter** home to ask parents for their help.

Now the process.

Multiplication Facts

How to Use This Book

Day 1, Learn the Squares

✓2 × 2 = 4   ✓6 × 6 = 36
✓3 × 3 = 9   ✓7 × 7 = 49
✓4 × 4 = 16   ✓8 × 8 = 64
✓5 × 5 = 25   ✓9 × 9 = 81

Why squares first? The answer is "we don't know," but for some reason the squares are easiest to learn. This encourages students because it builds confidence. I also like to solicit the parents' help and send **Letter A** (on page 19) to the parent or guardian. They will be eager to help and this saves classroom time normally used for more practice.

Use **Lesson 1** (on page 12) in class.

Day 2, Learn the Twos

Actually, there are only 7 facts to learn:

2 × 3 = 6   2 × 7 = 14
2 × 4 = 8   2 × 8 = 16
2 × 5 = 10   2 × 9 = 18
2 × 6 = 12

Why twos next? Two reasons:

1. They are easy to learn (probably because we frequently count by twos).

2. Again, this is an easy task that builds confidence.

Do **Lesson 2** (page 13) and send home **Letter B** (page 20). Review squares.

Day 3, Learn the Fives

5 × 6 = 30
5 × 7 = 35
5 × 8 = 40
5 × 9 = 45

Again, we learn fives next because they are easily learned and there are only four.

Do **Lesson 3** (page 14) and send home **Letter C** (page 21). Review squares and twos.

Day 4, Learn the Threes

3 × 4 = 12   3 × 7 = 21
3 × 5 = 15   3 × 8 = 24
3 × 6 = 18   3 × 9 = 27

Do **Lesson 4** (page 15) and send home **Letter D** (page 22). Review squares, twos and fives.

Day 5, Learn the Fours

$4 \times 5 = 20$

$4 \times 6 = 24$

$4 \times 7 = 28$

$4 \times 8 = 32$

$4 \times 9 = 36$

Do **Lesson 5** (page 16) and send home **Letter E** (page 23). Review squares, twos, fives and threes.

Day 6, Learn the Sixes, Sevens and Eights

$6 \times 7 = 42$	$7 \times 8 = 56$
$6 \times 8 = 48$	$7 \times 9 = 63$
$6 \times 9 = 54$	$8 \times 9 = 72$

Do **Lesson 6** (page 17) and send home **Letter F** (page 24). Review squares, twos, fives, threes and fours.

Day 7, All facts, review and test

Focus on the facts students still have trouble with. Send **Letter G** to parents (page 25).

That's it! Now the only other thing you need to do is to periodically review the learning. I strongly suggest using games.

Table 1

x	0	1	2	3	4	5	6	7	8	9
0	0	0	0	0	0	0	0	0	0	0
1	0	1	2	3	4	5	6	7	8	9
2	0	2	4	6	8	10	12	14	16	18
3	0	3	6	9	12	15	18	21	24	27
4	0	4	8	12	16	20	24	28	32	36
5	0	5	10	15	20	25	30	35	40	45
6	0	6	12	18	24	30	36	42	48	54
7	0	7	14	21	28	35	42	49	56	63
8	0	8	16	24	32	40	48	56	64	72
9	0	9	18	27	36	45	54	63	72	81

Table 2

x	0	1	2	3	4	5	6	7	8	9
0	0	0	0	0	0	0	0	0	0	0
1	0	1	2	3	4	5	6	7	8	9
2	0	2	4	6	8	10	12	14	16	18
3	0	3	6	9	12	15	18	21	24	27
4	0	4	8	12	16	20	24	28	32	36
5	0	5	10	15	20	25	30	35	40	45
6	0	6	12	18	24	30	36	42	48	54
7	0	7	14	21	28	35	42	49	56	63
8	0	8	16	24	32	40	48	56	64	72
9	0	9	18	27	36	45	54	63	72	81

Multiplication Table of Facts

Table 3

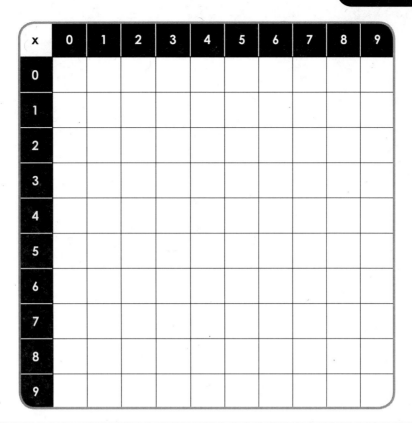

Multiplication Table of Facts

Table 3

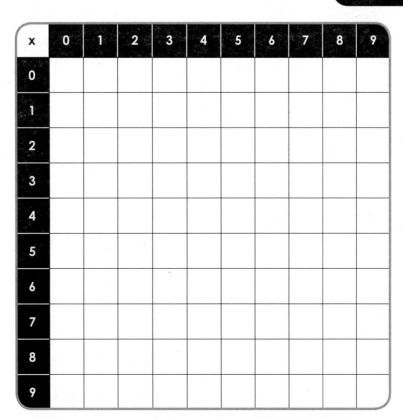

Multiplication Facts

Complete the following. If you need help, find the answers in your table.

1. 2 x 2 =

2. 3 x 3 =

3. 4 x 4 =

4. 5 x 5 =

5. 6 x 6 =

6. 7 x 7 =

7. 8 x 8 =

8. 9 x 9 =

9. 8 x 8 =

10. 7 x 7 =

11. 6 x 6 =

12. 5 x 5 =

13. 4 x 4 =

14. 3 x 3 =

15. 2 x 2 =

16. 2 x 2 =

17. 4 x 4 =

18. 6 x 6 =

19. 8 x 8 =

20. 3 x 3 =

21. 5 x 5 =

22. 7 x 7 =

23. 9 x 9 =

24. 2 x 2 =

25. 8 x 8 =

26. 9 x 9 =

27. 7 x 7 =

28. 3 x 3 =

29. 5 x 5 =

30. 6 x 6 =

31. 4 x 4 =

32. 6 x 6 =

33. 9 x 9 =

34. 5 x 5 =

35. 7 x 7 =

36. 8 x 8 =

37. 6 x 6 =

38. 4 x 4 =

39. 5 x 5 =

40. 7 x 7 =

41. 3 x 3 =

42. 7 x 7 =

43. 8 x 8 =

44. 4 x 4 =

45. 2 x 2 =

46. 9 x 9 =

47. 8 x 8 =

48. 3 x 3 =

49. 6 x 6 =

50. 9 x 9 =

Multiplication Facts — Lesson 2, Twos and Squares

Complete the following. If you need help, find the answers in your table.

1. $2 \times 3 =$

2. $2 \times 4 =$

3. $2 \times 5 =$

4. $2 \times 6 =$

5. $2 \times 7 =$

6. $2 \times 8 =$

7. $2 \times 9 =$

8. $2 \times 8 =$

9. $2 \times 7 =$

10. $2 \times 6 =$

11. $2 \times 5 =$

12. $2 \times 4 =$

13. $2 \times 3 =$

14. $2 \times 9 =$

15. $2 \times 3 =$

16. $2 \times 8 =$

17. $2 \times 4 =$

18. $2 \times 7 =$

19. $2 \times 6 =$

20. $2 \times 5 =$

21. $2 \times 2 =$

22. $2 \times 4 =$

23. $2 \times 6 =$

24. $2 \times 8 =$

25. $2 \times 3 =$

26. $2 \times 5 =$

27. $2 \times 7 =$

28. $2 \times 9 =$

29. $9 \times 9 =$

30. $7 \times 7 =$

31. $2 \times 2 =$

32. $8 \times 8 =$

33. $4 \times 4 =$

34. $9 \times 9 =$

35. $3 \times 3 =$

36. $6 \times 6 =$

37. $8 \times 8 =$

38. $6 \times 6 =$

39. $4 \times 4 =$

40. $5 \times 5 =$

41. $7 \times 7 =$

42. $2 \times 2 =$

43. $5 \times 5 =$

44. $3 \times 3 =$

45. $4 \times 4 =$

46. $6 \times 6 =$

47. $5 \times 5 =$

48. $7 \times 7 =$

49. $8 \times 8 =$

50. $9 \times 9 =$

Complete the following. If you need help, find the answers in your table.

#	Problem	#	Problem	#	Problem
1.	5 x 6 =	18.	2 x 3 =	35.	9 x 9 =
2.	5 x 7 =	19.	5 x 8 =	36.	5 x 8 =
3.	5 x 8 =	20.	2 x 4 =	37.	2 x 3 =
4.	5 x 9 =	21.	5 x 9 =	38.	8 x 8 =
5.	5 x 8 =	22.	2 x 5 =	39.	5 x 7 =
6.	5 x 7 =	23.	5 x 7 =	40.	2 x 6 =
7.	5 x 6 =	24.	2 x 6 =	41.	7 x 7 =
8.	5 x 5 =	25.	2 x 3 =	42.	5 x 6 =
9.	5 x 6 =	26.	2 x 7 =	43.	2 x 7 =
10.	6 x 6 =	27.	5 x 6 =	44.	6 x 6 =
11.	5 x 7 =	28.	2 x 8 =	45.	5 x 9 =
12.	7 x 7 =	29.	5 x 7 =	46.	2 x 4 =
13.	5 x 8 =	30.	2 x 9 =	47.	5 x 5 =
14.	8 x 8 =	31.	5 x 8 =	48.	2 x 8 =
15.	5 x 9 =	32.	2 x 2 =	49.	8 x 8 =
16.	9 x 9 =	33.	5 x 9 =	50.	2 x 9 =
17.	5 x 6 =	34.	2 x 5 =		

Multiplication Facts

Complete the following. If you need help, find the answers in your table.

1. 3 x 4 =	18. 2 x 6 =	35. 3 x 7 =
2. 3 x 5 =	19. 5 x 9 =	36. 7 x 7 =
3. 3 x 6 =	20. 2 x 7 =	37. 3 x 8 =
4. 3 x 7 =	21. 9 x 9 =	38. 3 x 5 =
5. 3 x 8 =	22. 2 x 8 =	39. 3 x 9 =
6. 3 x 9 =	23. 8 x 8 =	40. 8 x 8 =
7. 3 x 8 =	24. 2 x 9 =	41. 3 x 7 =
8. 3 x 7 =	25. 7 x 7 =	42. 3 x 6 =
9. 3 x 6 =	26. 6 x 6 =	43. 3 x 8 =
10. 3 x 5 =	27. 5 x 8 =	44. 3 x 7 =
11. 3 x 4 =	28. 5 x 5 =	45. 3 x 6 =
12. 2 x 3 =	29. 7 x 7 =	46. 3 x 9 =
13. 5 x 6 =	30. 3 x 3 =	47. 3 x 5 =
14. 2 x 4 =	31. 3 x 4 =	48. 4 x 4 =
15. 5 x 7 =	32. 3 x 5 =	49. 7 x 7 =
16. 2 x 5 =	33. 6 x 6 =	50. 9 x 9 =
17. 5 x 8 =	34. 3 x 6 =	

Multiplication Facts   Lesson 5, Fours and Review

Complete the following. If you need help, find the answers in your table.

1. 4 x 5 =

2. 4 x 6 =

3. 4 x 7 =

4. 4 x 8 =

5. 4 x 9 =

6. 4 x 8 =

7. 4 x 7 =

8. 4 x 6 =

9. 4 x 5 =

10. 4 x 4 =

11. 5 x 6 =

12. 5 x 5 =

13. 5 x 7 =

14. 6 x 6 =

15. 3 x 3 =

16. 7 x 7 =

17. 5 x 8 =

18. 8 x 8 =

19. 3 x 4 =

20. 9 x 9 =

21. 5 x 9 =

22. 3 x 5 =

23. 3 x 7 =

24. 3 x 9 =

25. 4 x 6 =

26. 4 x 9 =

27. 4 x 8 =

28. 4 x 6 =

29. 4 x 7 =

30. 4 x 5 =

31. 4 x 3 =

32. 4 x 2 =

33. 2 x 3 =

34. 4 x 7 =

35. 2 x 4 =

36. 4 x 8 =

37. 2 x 5 =

38. 3 x 8 =

39. 2 x 6 =

40. 4 x 9 =

41. 2 x 7 =

42. 4 x 7 =

43. 2 x 8 =

44. 4 x 8 =

45. 2 x 9 =

46. 3 x 6 =

47. 4 x 9 =

48. 9 x 9 =

49. 5 x 8 =

50. 4 x 9 =

Multiplication Facts

Complete the following. If you need help, find the answers in your table.

1. 6 x 7 =

2. 6 x 8 =

3. 6 x 9 =

4. 7 x 8 =

5. 7 x 9 =

6. 8 x 9 =

7. 7 x 9 =

8. 7 x 8 =

9. 6 x 9 =

10. 6 x 8 =

11. 6 x 7 =

12. 6 x 9 =

13. 6 x 8 =

14. 7 x 8 =

15. 7 x 9 =

16. 2 x 2 =

17. 6 x 9 =

18. 3 x 3 =

19. 7 x 8 =

20. 4 x 4 =

21. 3 x 7 =

22. 5 x 5 =

23. 4 x 8 =

24. 6 x 6 =

25. 6 x 7 =

26. 7 x 7 =

27. 4 x 5 =

28. 8 x 8 =

29. 4 x 6 =

30. 9 x 9 =

31. 6 x 8 =

32. 2 x 3 =

33. 8 x 9 =

34. 2 x 4 =

35. 3 x 9 =

36. 2 x 5 =

37. 6 x 7 =

38. 2 x 6 =

39. 7 x 9 =

40. 2 x 7 =

41. 3 x 8 =

42. 2 x 8 =

43. 4 x 7 =

44. 2 x 9 =

45. 4 x 9 =

46. 5 x 7 =

47. 5 x 8 =

48. 5 x 9 =

49. 7 x 9 =

50. 6 x 9 =

Multiplication Facts

Solve as quickly as you can. If you need help, find the answers in your table.

1. 2 x 2 =

2. 3 x 3 =

3. 4 x 4 =

4. 5 x 5 =

5. 6 x 6 =

6. 7 x 7 =

7. 8 x 8 =

8. 8 x 9 =

9. 2 x 3 =

10. 2 x 4 =

11. 2 x 5 =

12. 2 x 6 =

13. 2 x 7 =

14. 2 x 8 =

15. 2 x 9 =

16. 5 x 6 =

17. 5 x 7 =

18. 5 x 8 =

19. 5 x 9 =

20. 3 x 4 =

21. 3 x 5 =

22. 3 x 6 =

23. 3 x 7 =

24. 3 x 8 =

25. 3 x 9 =

26. 4 x 5 =

27. 4 x 6 =

28. 4 x 7 =

29. 4 x 8 =

30. 4 x 9 =

31. 6 x 7 =

32. 6 x 8 =

33. 6 x 9 =

34. 7 x 8 =

35. 7 x 9 =

36. 8 x 9 =

37. 7 x 6 =

38. 7 x 8 =

39. 9 x 4 =

40. 9 x 6 =

41. 9 x 7 =

42. 9 x 8 =

43. 6 x 7 =

44. 7 x 9 =

45. 8 x 7 =

46. 6 x 9 =

47. 8 x 5 =

48. 7 x 5 =

49. 9 x 6 =

50. 6 x 9 =

Dear parents,

Over the next seven days we are learning the multiplication facts. We are using a system called "Multiplication Facts in Seven Days." Each day I will send you some problems I want you to help your child master. Have your child master these facts (and these only), so that your child will know these facts by tomorrow. How you do this is up to you.

Today's facts

$2 \times 2 = 4$	$6 \times 6 = 36$
$3 \times 3 = 9$	$7 \times 7 = 49$
$4 \times 4 = 16$	$8 \times 8 = 64$
$5 \times 5 = 25$	$9 \times 9 = 81$

It is very important to learn the multiplication facts and I really appreciate your cooperation.

....

Teacher

Extra notes ....

....

....

....

....

Dear parents,

This is the second day in our series of lessons designed to teach your child all of the multiplication facts in seven days. Today I would like you to help your child learn the following facts:

Today's facts

2 x 3 = 6   2 x 7 = 14

2 x 4 = 8   2 x 8 = 16

2 x 5 = 10   2 x 9 = 18

2 x 6 = 12

Review the squares (below)

2 x 2 = 4   6 x 6 = 36

3 x 3 = 9   7 x 7 = 49

4 x 4 = 16   8 x 8 = 64

5 x 5 = 25   9 x 9 = 81

Thank you for your help,

....

Teacher

Extra notes ....

....

....

....

....

....

Dear parents,

Today we will continue your child's understanding of multiplication facts. On this third day, we are focusing on the multiplication facts below. Please drill these facts and review the previous facts (squares and twos):

Today's facts

5 x 6 = 30   5 x 8 = 40

5 x 7 = 35   5 x 9 = 45

Review the following

2 x 2 = 4	7 x 7 = 49	2 x 5 = 10
3 x 3 = 9	8 x 8 = 64	2 x 6 = 12
4 x 4 = 16	9 x 9 = 81	2 x 7 = 14
5 x 5 = 25	2 x 3 = 6	2 x 8 = 16
6 x 6 = 36	2 x 4 = 8	2 x 9 = 18

Thank you for your help,

_____

Teacher

Extra notes _____

_____

_____

_____

_____

Multiplication Facts

Dear parents,

This is the fourth day of our "Multiplication Facts in Seven Days."
Please drill the following facts:

Today's facts

3 x 4 = 12	3 x 6 = 18	3 x 8 = 24
3 x 5 = 15	3 x 7 = 21	3 x 9 = 27

Review the following

2 x 2 = 4	2 x 3 = 6	5 x 6 = 30
3 x 3 = 9	2 x 4 = 8	5 x 7 = 35
4 x 4 = 16	2 x 5 = 10	5 x 8 = 40
5 x 5 = 25	2 x 6 = 12	5 x 9 = 45
6 x 6 = 36	2 x 7 = 14	
7 x 7 = 49	2 x 8 = 16	
8 x 8 = 64	2 x 9 = 18	
9 x 9 = 81		

Thanks for your help,

....

Teacher

Extra notes ....

....

....

....

....

www.didax.com ~ ©Didax Educational Resources

Dear parents,

This is the fifth day your child is learning the multiplication facts. Please drill your child on the following facts:

Today's facts

4 x 5 = 20	4 x 7 = 28	4 x 8 = 32
4 x 6 = 24		4 x 9 = 36

Review the following

2 x 2 = 4	2 x 3 = 6	5 x 6 = 30
3 x 4 = 12	3 x 3 = 9	2 x 4 = 8
5 x 7 = 35	3 x 5 = 15	4 x 4 = 16
2 x 5 = 10	5 x 8 = 40	3 x 6 = 18
5 x 5 = 25	2 x 6 = 12	5 x 9 = 45
3 x 7 = 21	6 x 6 = 36	2 x 7 = 14
9 x 9 = 81	3 x 8 = 24	7 x 7 = 49
2 x 8 = 16	2 x 9 = 18	3 x 9 = 27
8 x 8 = 64		

Thanks for your help,

....

Teacher

Extra notes ....

....

....

....

Dear parents,

On this sixth day of learning the multiplication facts, your child is memorizing the following. Please drill your child on the following facts:

Today's facts

$6 \times 7 = 42$	$7 \times 8 = 56$	$8 \times 9 = 72$
$6 \times 8 = 48$	$7 \times 9 = 63$	$6 \times 9 = 54$

Review the following

$2 \times 2 = 4$	$2 \times 3 = 6$	$5 \times 6 = 30$
$3 \times 8 = 24$	$3 \times 3 = 9$	$2 \times 4 = 8$
$5 \times 7 = 35$	$3 \times 9 = 27$	$4 \times 4 = 16$
$2 \times 5 = 10$	$5 \times 8 = 40$	$4 \times 5 = 20$
$5 \times 5 = 25$	$2 \times 6 = 12$	$5 \times 9 = 45$
$4 \times 6 = 24$	$6 \times 6 = 36$	$2 \times 7 = 14$
$3 \times 4 = 12$	$4 \times 7 = 28$	$7 \times 7 = 49$
$2 \times 8 = 16$	$3 \times 5 = 15$	$4 \times 8 = 32$
$8 \times 8 = 64$	$2 \times 9 = 18$	$3 \times 6 = 18$
$4 \times 9 = 36$	$9 \times 9 = 81$	$3 \times 7 = 21$

Thank you for your help,

....

Teacher

Extra notes ....

....

....

Dear parents,

This is the last day in our series of "Multiplication Facts in Seven Days." All of the facts have been covered, but there may be a few your child needs to review and memorize. Below is a set of all the facts. See that your child knows the facts and spend extra time reviewing any that cause your child to hesitate or that they are unable to recall. Occasionally go back and review the facts.

Squares	Twos	Fives	Threes
2 x 2 = 4	2 x 3 = 6	5 x 6 = 30	3 x 4 = 2
3 x 3 = 9	2 x 4 = 8	5 x 7 = 35	3 x 5 = 15
4 x 4 = 16	2 x 5 = 10	5 x 8 = 40	3 x 6 = 18
5 x 5 = 25	2 x 6 = 12	5 x 9 = 45	3 x 7 = 21
6 x 6 = 36	2 x 7 = 14		3 x 8 = 24
7 x 7 = 49	2 x 8 = 16		3 x 9 = 27
8 x 8 = 64	2 x 9 = 18		
9 x 9 = 81			

Fours	Sixes	Sevens	Eights
4 x 5 = 20	6 x 7 = 42	7 x 8 = 56	8 x 9 = 72
4 x 6 = 24	6 x 8 = 48	7 x 9 = 63	
4 x 7 = 28	6 x 9 = 54		
4 x 8 = 32			
4 x 9 = 36			

Thank you for your help,

....

Teacher

Extra notes ....

....

....

Final Tests

Periodically give one of the final tests to the class to keep the facts fresh in their minds.

You may have the students time their test to see if they can improve their speed.

Randomly rotate the three tests.

Final Test A

1. $2 \times 2 =$

2. $3 \times 3 =$

3. $4 \times 4 =$

4. $5 \times 5 =$

5. $6 \times 6 =$

6. $7 \times 7 =$

Final Test B

1. $6 \times 6 =$

. $2 \times 4 =$

. $5 \times 6 =$

. $\times 4 =$

. $\times 6 =$

6. $3 \times 8 =$

Final Test C

1. $7 \times 6 =$

2. $2 \times 3 =$

. $3 \times 7 =$

$5 \times 2 =$

$4 \times 3 =$

$\times 4 =$

. $3 \times 2 =$

Multiplication Facts

1. 2 x 2 =

2. 3 x 3 =

3. 4 x 4 =

4. 5 x 5 =

5. 6 x 6 =

6. 7 x 7 =

7. 8 x 8 =

8. 9 x 9 =

9. 2 x 3 =

10. 2 x 4 =

11. 2 x 5 =

12. 2 x 6 =

13. 2 x 7 =

14. 2 x 8 =

15. 2 x 9 =

16. 5 x 6 =

17. 5 x 7 =

18. 5 x 8 =

19. 5 x 9 =

20. 3 x 4 =

21. 3 x 5 =

22. 3 x 6 =

23. 3 x 7 =

24. 3 x 8 =

25. 3 x 9 =

26. 4 x 5 =

27. 4 x 6 =

28. 4 x 7 =

29. 4 x 8 =

30. 4 x 9 =

31. 6 x 7 =

32. 6 x 8 =

33. 6 x 9 =

34. 7 x 8 =

35. 7 x 9 =

36. 8 x 9 =

1. 6 x 6 =

2. 2 x 4 =

3. 5 x 6 =

4. 3 x 4 =

5. 4 x 6 =

6. 3 x 8 =

7. 2 x 2 =

8. 5 x 8 =

9. 4 x 8 =

10. 6 x 7 =

11. 2 x 8 =

12. 7 x 8 =

13. 9 x 9 =

14. 2 x 6 =

15. 3 x 9 =

16. 6 x 8 =

17. 8 x 8 =

18. 7 x 9 =

19. 8 x 9 =

20. 4 x 5 =

21. 3 x 6 =

22. 7 x 7 =

23. 2 x 7 =

24. 6 x 9 =

25. 2 x 9 =

26. 3 x 5 =

27. 5 x 5 =

28. 2 x 3 =

29. 5 x 7 =

30. 4 x 7 =

31. 5 x 9 =

32. 4 x 4 =

33. 2 x 5 =

34. 4 x 9 =

35. 3 x 3 =

36. 3 x 7 =

Multiplication Facts

Final Test C

1. 7 x 6 =

2. 2 x 3 =

3. 3 x 7 =

4. 5 x 2 =

5. 4 x 3 =

6. 2 x 4 =

7. 3 x 2 =

8. 6 x 9 =

9. 7 x 4 =

10. 8 x 5 =

11. 2 x 5 =

12. 3 x 4 =

13. 8 x 8 =

14. 3 x 8 =

15. 9 x 2 =

16. 6 x 6 =

17. 7 x 5 =

18. 8 x 6 =

19. 4 x 8 =

20. 9 x 8 =

21. 9 x 9 =

22. 5 x 8 =

23. 7 x 9 =

24. 8 x 6 =

25. 7 x 7 =

26. 4 x 9 =

27. 7 x 9 =

28. 9 x 4 =

29. 3 x 3 =

30. 4 x 2 =

31. 5 x 3 =

32. 6 x 3 =

33. 8 x 2 =

34. 6 x 8 =

35. 9 x 4 =

36. 2 x 2 =

37. 7 x 3 =

38. 9 x 6 =

39. 5 x 5 =

40. 3 x 5 =

41. 4 x 6 =

42. 4 x 7 =

Multiplication Facts in Seven Days

©Didax Educational Resources ~ www.didax.com

43. 3 x 9 =

44. 8 x 7 =

45. 7 x 6 =

46. 6 x 5 =

47. 8 x 7 =

48. 9 x 7 =

49. 7 x 5 =

50. 9 x 6 =

51. 4 x 9 =

52. 6 x 9 =

53. 6 x 7 =

54. 6 x 8 =

55. 8 x 7 =

56. 9 x 3 =

57. 8 x 3 =

58. 7 x 8 =

59. 2 x 8 =

60. 6 x 2 =

61. 9 x 5 =

62. 7 x 6 =

63. 9 x 7 =

64. 2 x 7 =

65. 5 x 6 =

66. 5 x 4 =

67. 7 x 2 =

68. 3 x 6 =

69. 2 x 6 =

70. 4 x 5 =

71. 6 x 4 =

72. 8 x 4 =

73. 4 x 4 =

74. 9 x 3 =

75. 2 x 9 =

76. 9 x 6 =

77. 9 x 7 =

78. 7 x 9 =

79. 5 x 7 =

80. 4 x 7 =

81. 8 x 9 =

82. 7 x 6 =

83. 9 x 8 =

84. 5 x 9 =

x	0	1	2	3	4	5	6	7	8	9
0	0	0	0	0	0	0	0	0	0	0
1	0	1	2	3	4	5	6	7	8	9
2	0	2	4	6	8	10	12	14	16	18
3	0	3	6	9	12	15	18	21	24	27
4	0	4	8	12	16	20	24	28	32	36
5	0	5	10	15	20	25	30	35	40	45
6	0	6	12	18	24	30	36	42	48	54
7	0	7	14	21	28	35	42	49	56	63
8	0	8	16	24	32	40	48	56	64	72
9	0	9	18	27	36	45	54	63	72	81

x	0	1	2	3	4	5	6	7	8	9
0	0	0	0	0	0	0	0	0	0	0
1	0	1	2	3	4	5	6	7	8	9
2	0	2	4	6	8	10	12	14	16	18
3	0	3	6	9	12	15	18	21	24	27
4	0	4	8	12	16	20	24	28	32	36
5	0	5	10	15	20	25	30	35	40	45
6	0	6	12	18	24	30	36	42	48	54
7	0	7	14	21	28	35	42	49	56	63
8	0	8	16	24	32	40	48	56	64	72
9	0	9	18	27	36	45	54	63	72	81

x	0	1	2	3	4	5	6	7	8	9
0	0	0	0	0	0	0	0	0	0	0
1	0	1	2	3	4	5	6	7	8	9
2	0	2	4	6	8	10	12	14	16	18
3	0	3	6	9	12	15	18	21	24	27
4	0	4	8	12	16	20	24	28	32	36
5	0	5	10	15	20	25	30	35	40	45
6	0	6	12	18	24	30	36	42	48	54
7	0	7	14	21	28	35	42	49	56	63
8	0	8	16	24	32	40	48	56	64	72
9	0	9	18	27	36	45	54	63	72	81

x	0	1	2	3	4	5	6	7	8	9
0	0	0	0	0	0	0	0	0	0	0
1	0	1	2	3	4	5	6	7	8	9
2	0	2	4	6	8	10	12	14	16	18
3	0	3	6	9	12	15	18	21	24	27
4	0	4	8	12	16	20	24	28	32	36
5	0	5	10	15	20	25	30	35	40	45
6	0	6	12	18	24	30	36	42	48	54
7	0	7	14	21	28	35	42	49	56	63
8	0	8	16	24	32	40	48	56	64	72
9	0	9	18	27	36	45	54	63	72	81

x	0	1	2	3	4	5	6	7	8	9
0	0	0	0	0	0	0	0	0	0	0
1	0	1	2	3	4	5	6	7	8	9
2	0	2	4	6	8	10	12	14	16	18
3	0	3	6	9	12	15	18	21	24	27
4	0	4	8	12	16	20	24	28	32	36
5	0	5	10	15	20	25	30	35	40	45
6	0	6	12	18	24	30	36	42	48	54
7	0	7	14	21	28	35	42	49	56	63
8	0	8	16	24	32	40	48	56	64	72
9	0	9	18	27	36	45	54	63	72	81

x	0	1	2	3	4	5	6	7	8	9
0	0	0	0	0	0	0	0	0	0	0
1	0	1	2	3	4	5	6	7	8	9
2	0	2	4	6	8	10	12	14	16	18
3	0	3	6	9	12	15	18	21	24	27
4	0	4	8	12	16	20	24	28	32	36
5	0	5	10	15	20	25	30	35	40	45
6	0	6	12	18	24	30	36	42	48	54
7	0	7	14	21	28	35	42	49	56	63
8	0	8	16	24	32	40	48	56	64	72
9	0	9	18	27	36	45	54	63	72	81

Answers

Fact Tests

Lesson 1, Squares..........pg 12

#	Ans	#	Ans
1.	4	26.	81
2.	9	27.	49
3.	16	28.	9
4.	25	29.	25
5.	36	30.	36
6.	49	31.	16
7.	64	32.	36
8.	81	33.	81
9.	64	34.	25
10.	49	35.	49
11.	36	36.	64
12.	25	37.	36
13.	16	38.	16
14.	9	39.	25
15.	4	40.	49
16.	4	41.	9
17.	16	42.	49
18.	36	43.	64
19.	64	44.	16
20.	9	45.	4
21.	25	46.	81
22.	49	47.	64
23.	81	48.	9
24.	4	49.	36
25.	64	50.	81

Lesson 2, Twos and Squares..................pg 13

#	Ans	#	Ans
1.	6	26.	10
2.	8	27.	14
3.	10	28.	18
4.	12	29.	81
5.	14	30.	49
6.	16	31.	4
7.	18	32.	64
8.	14	33.	16
9.	14	34.	81
10.	12	35.	9
11.	10	36.	36
12.	8	37.	64
13.	6	38.	36
14.	18	39.	16
15.	6	40.	25
16.	16	41.	49
17.	8	42.	4
18.	14	43.	25
19.	12	44.	9
20.	10	45.	16
21.	4	46.	36
22.	8	47.	25
23.	12	48.	49
24.	16	49.	64
25.	6	50.	81

Lesson 3, Fives and Review...............pg 14

#	Ans	#	Ans
1.	30	26.	14
2.	35	27.	30
3.	40	28.	16
4.	45	29.	35
5.	40	30.	18
6.	35	31.	40
7.	30	32.	4
8.	25	33.	45
9.	30	34.	10
10.	36	35.	81
11.	35	36.	40
12.	49	37.	6
13.	40	38.	64
14.	64	39.	35
15.	45	40.	12
16.	81	41.	49
17.	30	42.	30
18.	6	43.	14
19.	40	44.	36
20.	8	45.	45
21.	45	46.	8
22.	10	47.	25
23.	35	48.	16
24.	12	49.	64
25.	6	50.	18

Lesson 4, Threes and Review ....pg 15

#	Ans	#	Ans
1.	12	26.	36
2.	15	27.	40
3.	18	28.	25
4.	21	29.	49
5.	24	30.	9
6.	27	31.	12
7.	24	32.	15
8.	21	33.	36
9.	18	34.	18
10.	15	35.	21
11.	12	36.	49
12.	6	37.	24
13.	30	38.	15
14.	8	39.	27
15.	35	40.	64
16.	10	41.	21
17.	40	42.	18
18.	12	43.	24
19.	45	44.	21
20.	14	45.	18
21.	81	46.	27
22.	16	47.	15
23.	64	48.	16
24.	18	49.	49
25.	49	50.	81

Lesson 5, Fours and Review ....pg 16

#	Ans	#	Ans
1.	20	26.	36
2.	24	27.	32
3.	28	28.	24
4.	32	29.	28
5.	36	30.	20
6.	32	31.	12
7.	28	32.	8
8.	24	33.	6
9.	20	34.	28
10.	16	35.	8
11.	30	36.	32
12.	25	37.	10
13.	35	38.	24
14.	36	39.	12
15.	9	40.	36
16.	49	41.	14
17.	40	42.	28
18.	64	43.	16
19.	12	44.	32
20.	81	45.	18
21.	45	46.	18
22.	15	47.	36
23.	21	48.	81
24.	27	49.	40
25.	24	50.	6

Lesson 6, Sixes, Sevens Eights and Review..... pg 17

#	Ans	#	Ans
1.	42	26.	49
2.	48	27.	20
3.	54	28.	64
4.	56	29.	24
5.	63	30.	81
6.	72	31.	48
7.	63	32.	6
8.	56	33.	72
9.	54	34.	8
10.	48	35.	18
11.	42	36.	10
12.	54	37.	42
13.	48	38.	12
14.	56	39.	63
15.	63	40.	14
16.	4	41.	24
17.	54	42.	16
18.	9	43.	28
19.	56	44.	18
20.	16	45.	36
21.	21	46.	35
22.	25	47.	40
23.	32	48.	45
24.	36	49.	63
25.	42	50.	54

Lesson 7, Cumulative Review.....................pg 18

#	Ans	#	Ans
1.	4	10.	8
2.	9	11.	10
3.	16	12.	12
4.	25	13.	14
5.	36	14.	16
6.	49	15.	18
7.	64	16.	30
8.	72	17.	35
9.	6	18.	40
19.	45	35.	63
20.	12	36.	72
21.	15	37.	42
22.	18	38.	56
23.	21	39.	36
24.	24	40.	54
25.	27	41.	63
26.	20	42.	72
27.	24	43.	42
28.	28	44.	63
29.	32	45.	56
30.	36	46.	54
31.	42	47.	40
32.	48	48.	35
33.	54	49.	54
34.	56	50.	54

Final Tests

Final Test A ....pg 27

#	Ans	#	Ans
1.	4	19.	45
2.	9	20.	12
3.	16	21.	15
4.	25	22.	18
5.	36	23.	21
6.	49	24.	24
7.	64	25.	27
8.	81	26.	20
9.	6	27.	24
10.	8	28.	28
11.	10	29.	32
12.	12	30.	36
13.	14	31.	42
14.	16	32.	48
15.	18	33.	54
16.	30	34.	56
17.	35	35.	63
18.	40	36.	72

Final Test B ....pg 28

#	Ans	#	Ans
1.	36	19.	72
2.	8	20.	20
3.	30	21.	18
4.	12	22.	49
5.	24	23.	14
6.	24	24.	54
7.	4	25.	18
8.	40	26.	15
9.	32	27.	25
10.	42	28.	6
11.	16	29.	35
12.	56	30.	28
13.	81	31.	45
14.	12	32.	16
15.	27	33.	10
16.	48	34.	36
17.	64	35.	9
18.	63	36.	21

Final Test C ....pg 29-30

#	Ans	#	Ans
1.	42	3.	21
2.	6	4.	10
5.	12	46.	30
6.	8	47.	56
7.	6	48.	63
8.	54	49.	35
9.	28	50.	54
10.	40	51.	36
11.	10	52.	54
12.	12	53.	42
13.	64	54.	48
14.	24	55.	56
15.	18	56.	27
16.	36	57.	24
17.	35	58.	56
18.	48	59.	16
19.	32	60.	12
20.	72	61.	45
21.	81	62.	42
22.	40	63.	63
23.	63	64.	14
24.	48	65.	30
25.	49	66.	20
26.	36	67.	14
27.	63	68.	18
28.	6	69.	12
29.	9	70.	20
30.	8	71.	24
31.	15	72.	32
32.	18	73.	16
33.	16	74.	27
34.	48	75.	18
35.	36	76.	54
36.	4	77.	63
37.	21	78.	63
38.	54	79.	35
39.	25	80.	28
40.	15	81.	72
41.	24	82.	42
42.	28	83.	72
43.	27	84.	45